THE

C000177475

X-RATED
CARTOONS

BY ALLAN PLENDERLEITH

RAVETTE PUBLISHING

First published in 2002
Reprinted in 2003, 2004, 2005, 2007
Ravette Publishing Limited
Unit 3, Tristar Centre
Star Road, Partridge Green
West Sussex RH13 8RA

THE ODD SQUAD and all related characters
© 2002 by Allan Plenderleith

Printed in Malta by Gutenberg Press

ISBN: 978 1 84161 141 9

JEFF TRIES
TO CONVINCE
THE OFFICER
THAT THESE
ARE, IN FACT,
AIRBAGS.

JEFF TRIES
TO IMPROVE
MAUDE'S 'HAND
TECHNIQUE' BY
BLOCKING UP
THE KETCHUP
BOTTLE.

WHEN THE GIRL TOOK HER CLOTHES OFF, DUG WAS SURPRISED TO FIND SHE HAD AN ENORMOUS MUFF.

JEFF COULDN'T
WORK OUT
WHY 'BERTY
BIG NOSE'
ALWAYS SEEMED
TO HAVE TWO
GIRLFRIENDS.

MAUDE
REALISES IT'S
TIME TO DO
HER BIKINI LINE
AGAIN.

JEFF GETS A NASTY SURPRISE WHILST BLOWING UP HIS NEW BLOW-UP DOLL.

FORTUNATELY, MAUDE'S MAIL ORDER 'SEX PACK' ARRIVED IN A DISCREET BROWN PAPER PACKAGE.

DUG'S MUM
WALKS INTO THE
ROOM WHILE
HE WAS
'CHOKING THE
CHICKEN'.

MAUDE HAD
A FEELING
JEFF HAD BEEN
LOOKING AT
INTERNET PORN
AGAIN.

AS IF LOSING
HIS KEYS AND
HAVING TO CLIMB
THROUGH THE CAT
FLAP WASN'T BAD
ENOUGH, JEFF'S
PROBLEMS WERE
ABOUT TO BECOME
A WHOLE LOT
WORSE.

NEVER BLOW
OFF IN THE
DOGGY POSITION.

ONCE AGAIN,
THE DOG
HAD WORMS.

BORED OF
READY SALTED
CRISPS, JEFF
DECIDES TO
MAKE THEM
CHEESY
FLAVOUR.

ALWAYS MAKE
SURE SEXUAL
AIDS ARE
REMOVED
AFTER USE.

JEFF FINALLY AGREES THAT IT'S TIME TO TAKE THE DOG OUT FOR A WALK.

JEFF WOULD
SOON DISCOVER
THIS WOULD BE
THE LAST TIME
HE WOULD BE
ALLOWED TO
PRACTICE HIS
GOLF TECHNIQUE
IN THE HOUSE.

JEFF INVENTS A NEW GAME: 'DUNK FOR THE <u>REAL</u> LOVE SAUSAGE'.

DUG HAD A
CUNNING IDEA
TO GET HIS
GIRLFRIEND TO
GO 'DOWN
SOUTH'.

MAUDE FINALLY
PLUCKS UP THE
COURAGE TO
SHOW JEFF HER
HAIRY RING.

AFTER MANY YEARS TOGETHER, DOGS AND THEIR OWNERS BEGIN TO COPY ONE ANOTHER'S BEHAVIOUR.

JEFF VISITS THE
DOCTOR'S TO
HAVE A MOLE
REMOVED.

ONE OF THE MANY ADVANTAGES OF HAVING A LONG DONG: BEING ABLE TO PEE IN PUBLIC WITHOUT ANYONE NOTICING.

ALTHOUGH MAUDE WANTED JEFF TO SHOW HIS TRUE FEELINGS FOR HER IN PUBLIC, THIS WASN'T WHAT SHE MEANT.

BILLY FINDS A
NEW TOY IN HIS
MUM'S BEDROOM.

HAVING RUN OUT
OF CONDOMS,
JEFF IMPROVISES.

MAUDE USES THE
FUNNY TUMMY
SHE PICKED UP ON
HOLIDAY TO HER
ADVANTAGE.

MAUDE GOES
OUT WITH A
MAN WITH A
HUGE PECKER.

TIRED OF USING
A POOPER
SCOOPER,
JEFF COMES
UP WITH A
BETTER IDEA.

WHO NEEDS
NIPPLE TASSELS
WHEN YOU HAVE
OVERGROWN
NIPPLE HAIR!

EVEN WHEN SHE'S
PISSED, MAUDE
CAN STILL TAKE
HER FACE OFF.

HE MAY HAVE
HAD TO RESORT
TO DRASTIC
MEASURES,
BUT AT LEAST
BRENDA'S BRA
WAS FINALLY
OFF.

STRANGE – JEFF WAS <u>SURE</u> HIS TIPPEX WAS NEARLY FINISHED WHEN HE LEFT THE ROOM, BUT NOW IT WAS ALMOST FULL.

JEFF'S DOG
DISCOVERS
'SUZIE' WAS
<u>NOT</u> A TRUE
BLONDE
AFTER ALL.

JEFF KNEW
HE HAD TO
HAVE SEX
...AND SOON!

JEFF HAD A
FUNNY FEELING
THE KEBAB
WASN'T
ENTIRELY
LAMB.

BILLY'S NEW
MONEY–MAKING
SCHEME DID
NOT PROVE TOO
POPULAR WITH
THE GIRLS.

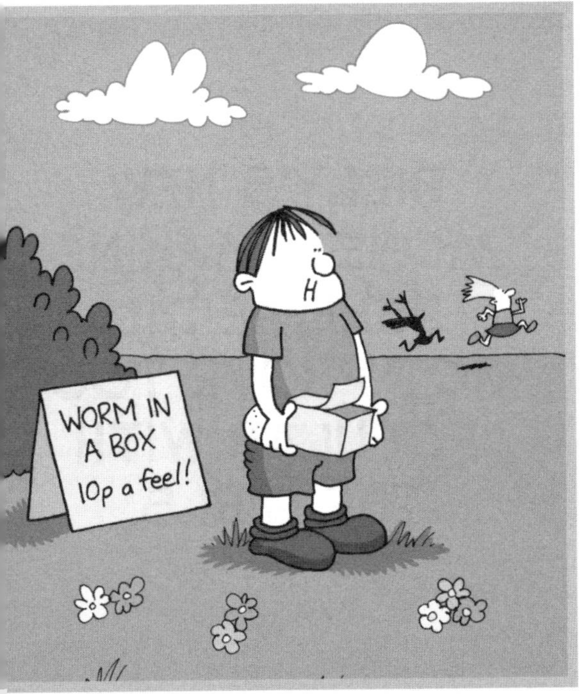
WORM IN
A BOX
10p a feel!

JEFF WAKES
UP WITH A
REAL STIFFIE.

DUG'S DATE WITH 'BARBARA' WAS GOING GREAT, UNTIL THE TAXI LIGHTS SHONE THROUGH HER DRESS.

WHEN JEFF HAD
ASKED TO 'GO
DOWN THE BIG
BROWN TUNNEL OF
LOVE', MAUDE WAS
RELIEVED TO FIND
IT <u>WASN'T</u>
A METAPHOR.

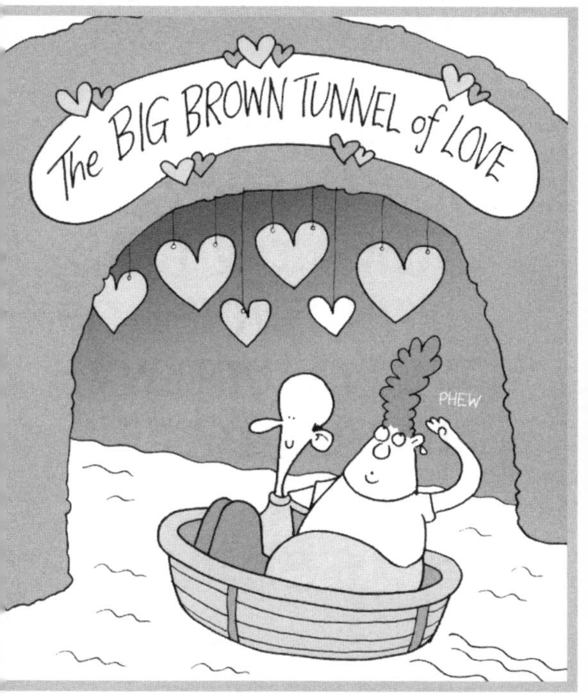
The BIG BROWN TUNNEL of LOVE
PHEW

FOLLOWING
THE SUCCESS OF
'CASUAL DRESS
FRIDAY',
THE COMPANY
INTRODUCES
'CASUAL SEX
TUESDAY'.

IN ONE HORRIBLE
MOMENT, MAUDE
DISCOVERS
WHY HER HEELS
SQUEAKED AND
WHERE LITTLE
FLUFFY HAD
GONE.

DUG HAD HEARD
YOUNG MEN
SHOULD EXERCISE
4 TO 5 TIMES
EVERY WEEK AND
BREAK A SWEAT.

MAUDE HAD THAT
CONSTIPATED
LOOK ON HER
FACE AGAIN.

MAUDE WAS
HORRIFIED TO
DISCOVER
JEFF'S
JAZZ MAGS.

JEFF DECIDES IT'S BEST TO KEEP THE LIGHTS ON DURING SEX.

SUDDENLY LILY
DECIDES TO
SERVE THE HAM
FOR CHRISTMAS
DINNER.